# Get Your Skates On!

by **Katie Dale**
illustrated by **Gareth Robinson**

Ron was often late.

He was late getting up.

He was late for the bus.

Get your skates on, Ron!

He was late for hockey.

Get your skates on, Ron!

Until one day Ron's nan got him...

At the start, it was a bit hard.

But soon Ron got the hang of them!

Now he was never late!

He zoomed in his bedroom...

Zoom!

...and he zoomed in the bathroom.

He zoomed on the bus!

When the bus set off,

Ron slid to the back.

Zoom!

Then when the bus stopped,
Ron slid back to the door!
Zoom!

13

Next, he took up roller hockey!

Zoom! Zoom! Zoom!

Ron never took his skates off.

But then Ron took his dog to the park.

The dog spotted a cat!

The cat ran down a big hill...

...and Ron slid after them!

Faster and faster, Ron slid.

Ron zoomed down the hill.

He zoomed past the bus stop...

...and he zoomed down his street.

Ron zoomed faster and faster and faster, until...

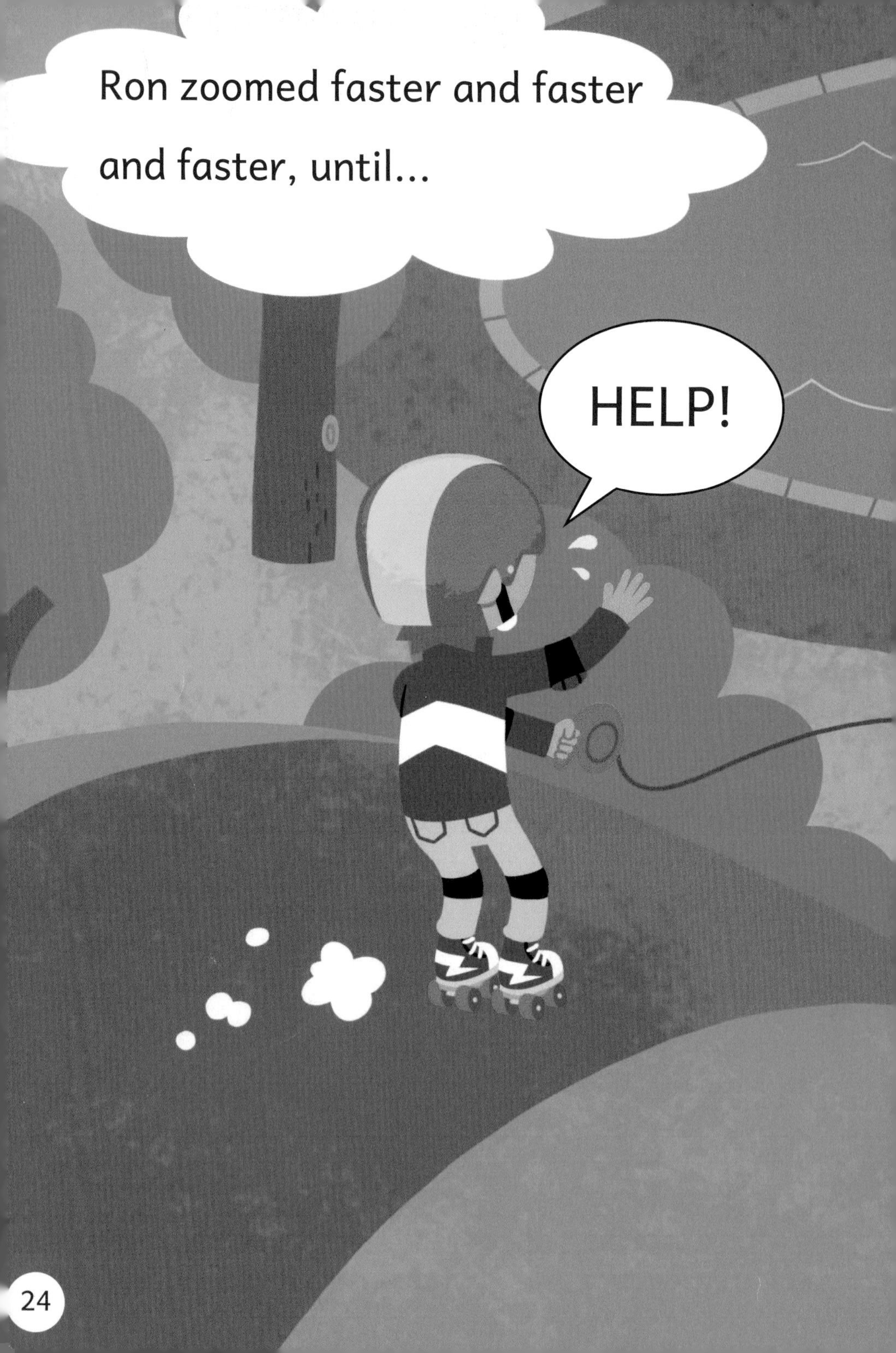

27

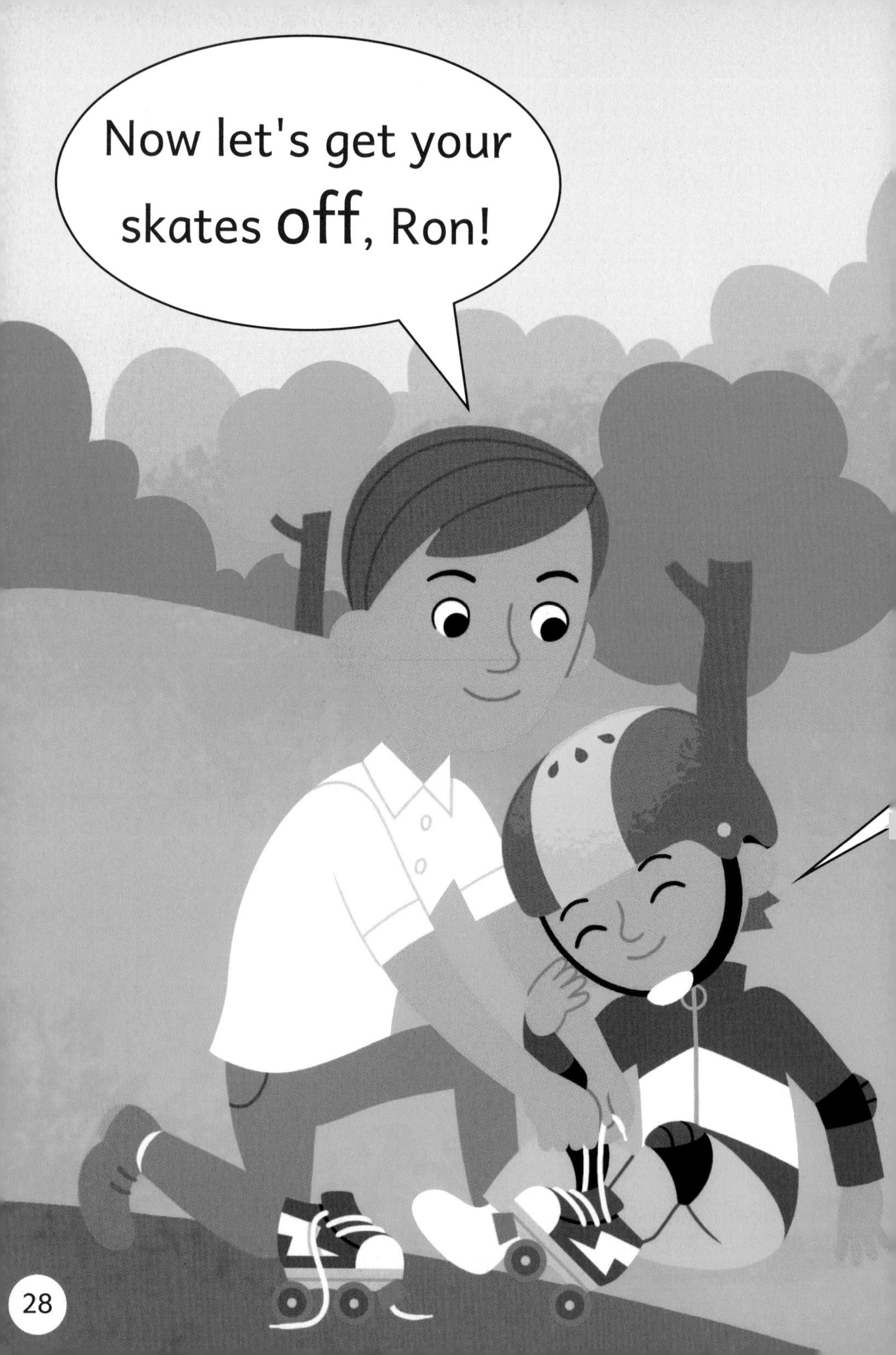
Now let's get your skates off, Ron!

# Quiz

1. Ron was often...
a) Busy
b) Late
c) Jumping

2. Who got Ron the skates?
a) His mum
b) His dad
c) His nan

3. What sport did Ron try?
a) Roller hockey
b) Ice skating
c) Roller basketball

4. Ron _____ down the hill.

a) Ran

b) Zoomed

c) Jumped

5. Who stopped Ron?

a) His dad

b) His nan

c) His mum

*Turn over for answers*

# Book Bands for Guided Reading

The Institute of Education book banding system is a scale of colours that reflects the various levels of reading difficulty. The bands are assigned by taking into account the content, the language style, the layout and phonics. Word, phrase and sentence level work is also taken into consideration.

Maverick Early Readers are a bright, attractive range of books covering the pink to white bands. All of these books have been book banded for guided reading to the industry standard and edited by a leading educational consultant.

To view the whole Maverick Readers scheme, visit our website at

www.maverickearlyreaders.com

Or scan the QR code above to view our scheme instantly!

*Quiz Answers: 1b, 2c, 3a, 4b, 5a*